SPREAD YOUR WINGS AND FLY
BLACK WOMEN FAIRIES COLORING BOOK

N. D. JONES

KUUMBA
PUBLISHING
CREATIVE MINDS
PASSIONATE HEARTS

Baltimore, Maryland

Kuumba Publishing
1325 Bedford Avenue
#32374
Pikesville, MD
kuumbapublishing.com

Cover Designer: Lily Dormishev
Fairies Illustrator and Cover Colorist: Ika Sirana
Frames Illustrator: Ekra Design

Spread Your Wings and Fly: Black Women Fairies Coloring Book/ N.D. Jones. -- 1st ed.
ISBN: 978-1-7352998-5-3

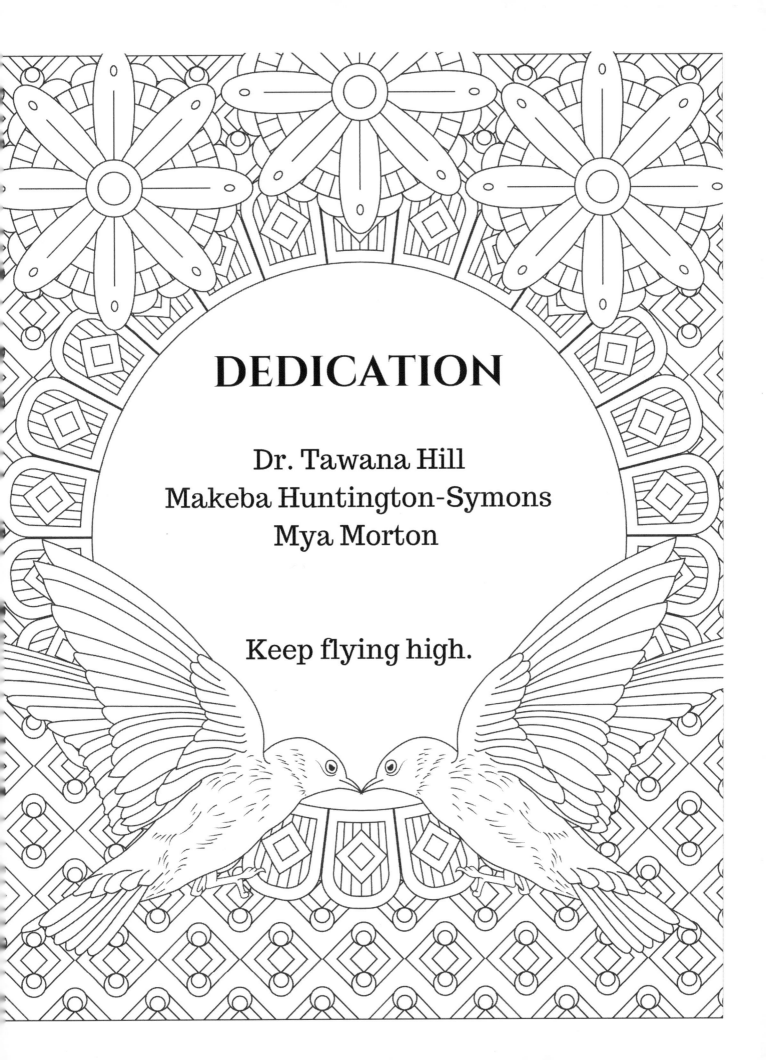

DEDICATION

Dr. Tawana Hill
Makeba Huntington-Symons
Mya Morton

Keep flying high.

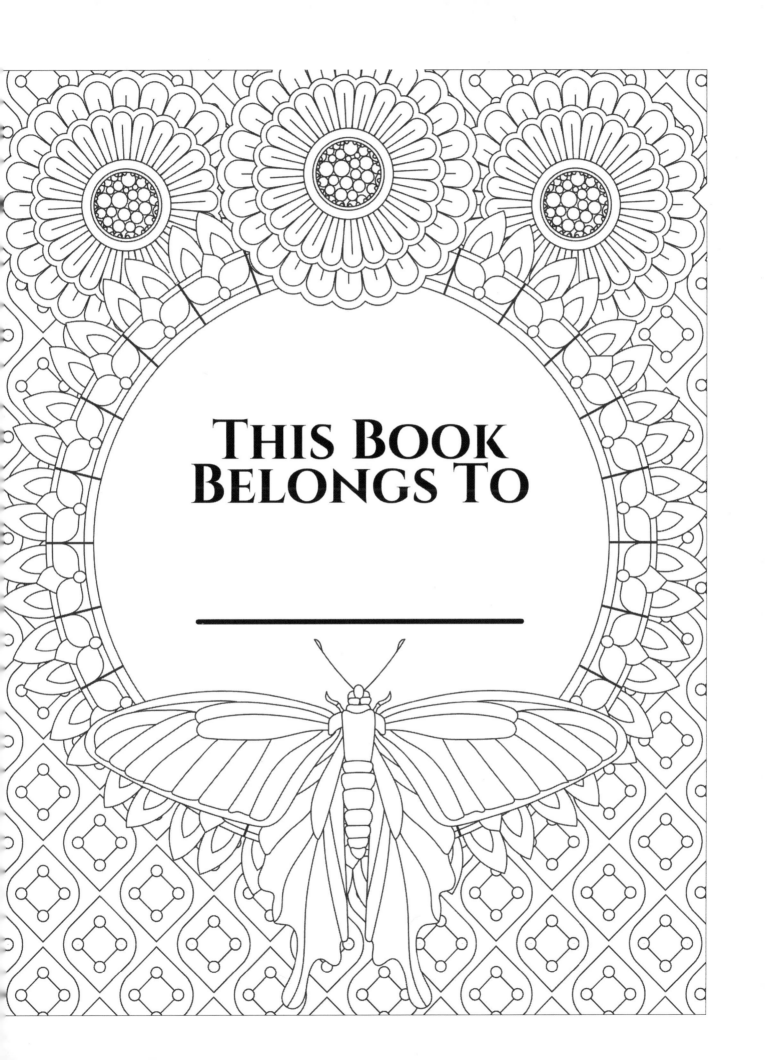

This Book Belongs To

_____

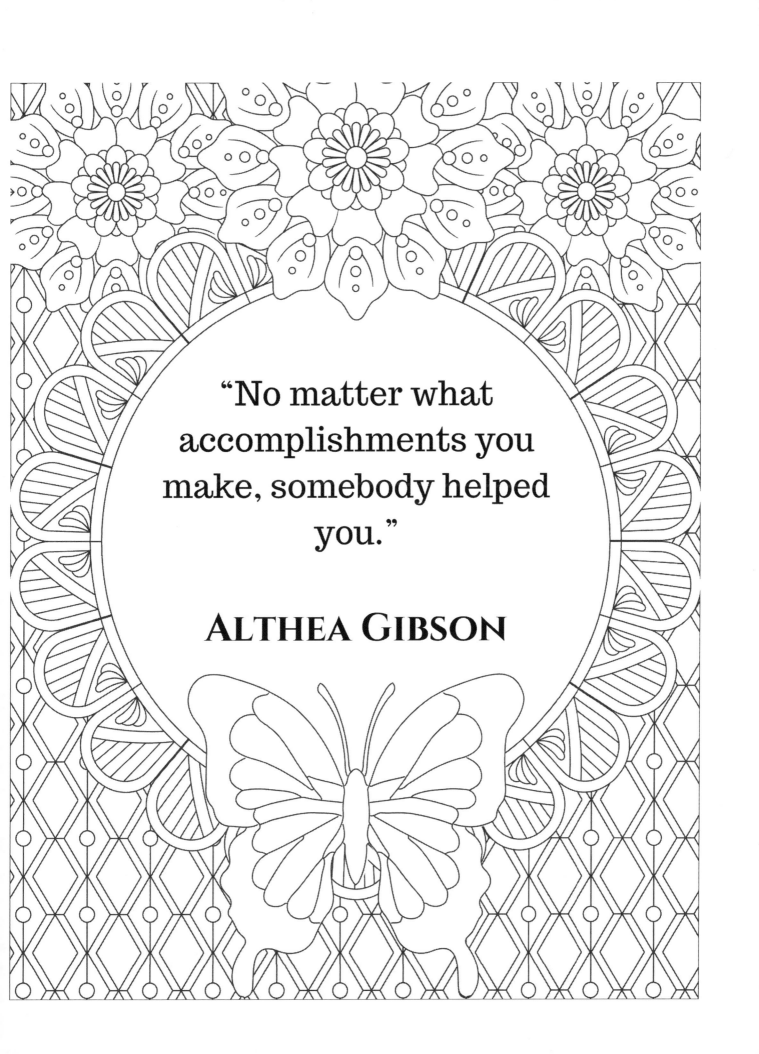

"No matter what accomplishments you make, somebody helped you."

ALTHEA GIBSON

February
Lucky & Loyal

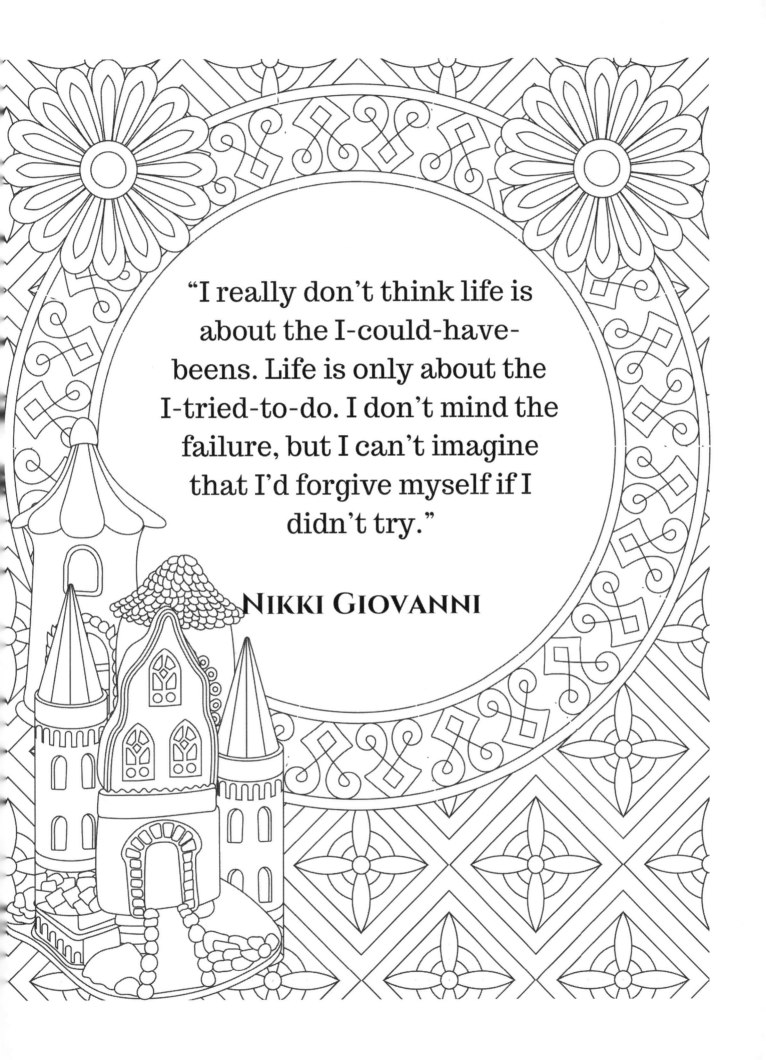

"I really don't think life is about the I-could-have-beens. Life is only about the I-tried-to-do. I don't mind the failure, but I can't imagine that I'd forgive myself if I didn't try."

NIKKI GIOVANNI

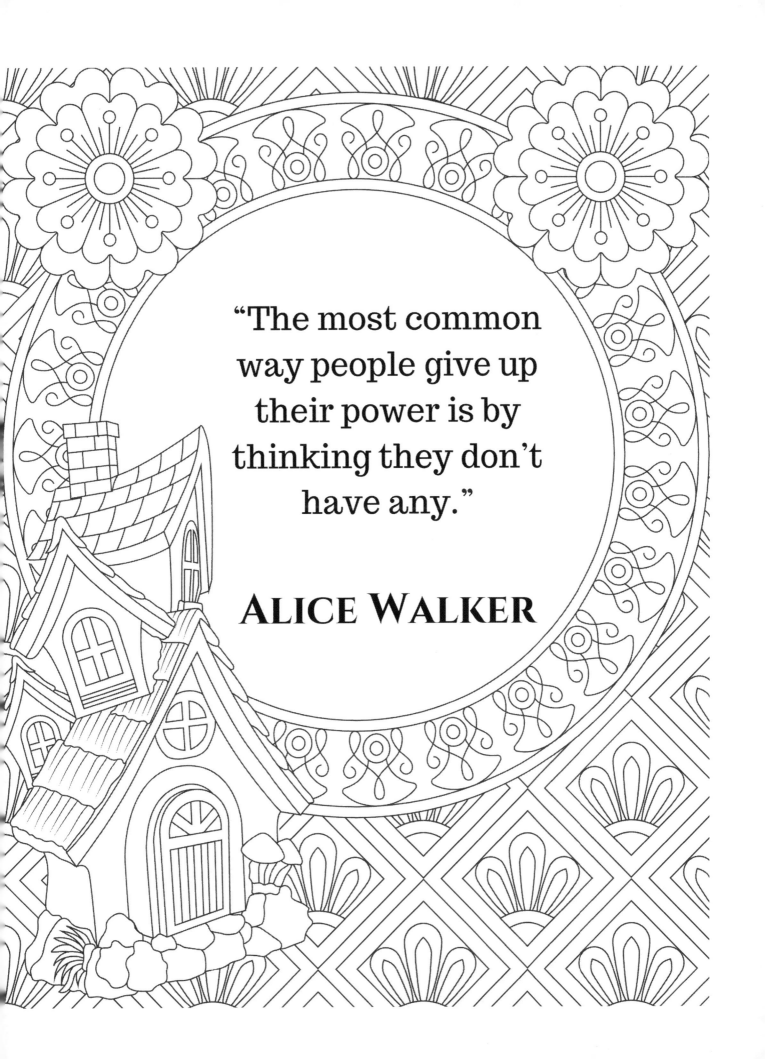

"The most common way people give up their power is by thinking they don't have any."

ALICE WALKER

April

Caring & Strong

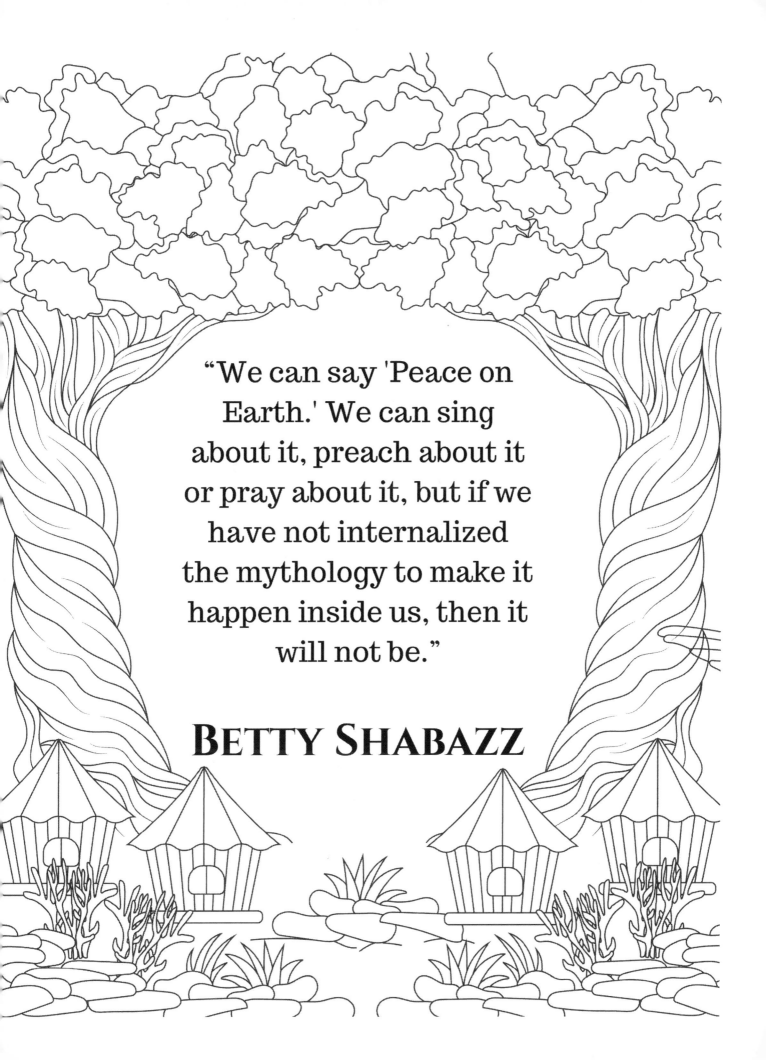

"We can say 'Peace on Earth.' We can sing about it, preach about it or pray about it, but if we have not internalized the mythology to make it happen inside us, then it will not be."

BETTY SHABAZZ

May

Loving & Practical

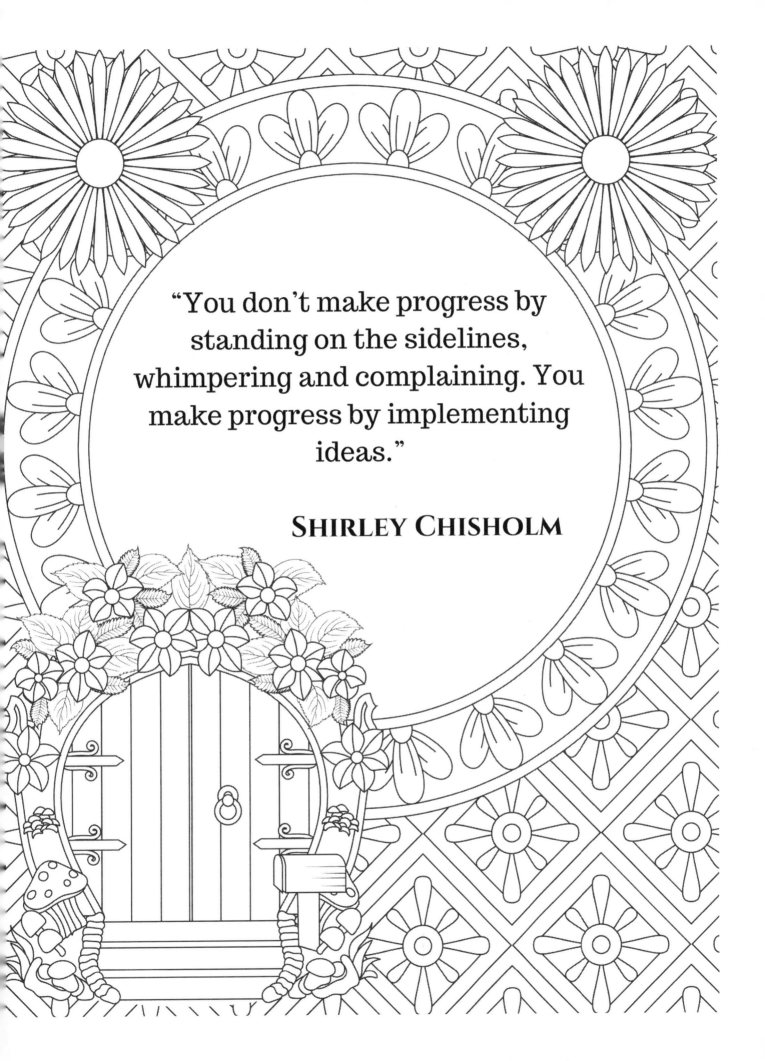

"You don't make progress by standing on the sidelines, whimpering and complaining. You make progress by implementing ideas."

SHIRLEY CHISHOLM

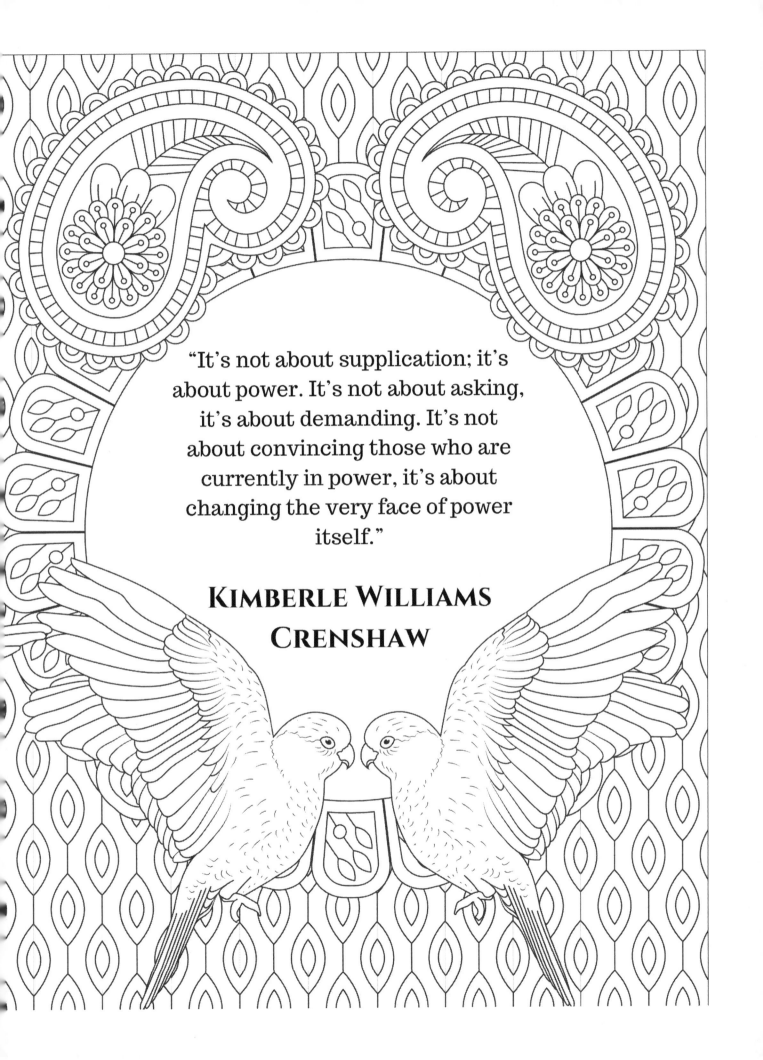

"It's not about supplication; it's about power. It's not about asking, it's about demanding. It's not about convincing those who are currently in power, it's about changing the very face of power itself."

KIMBERLE WILLIAMS CRENSHAW

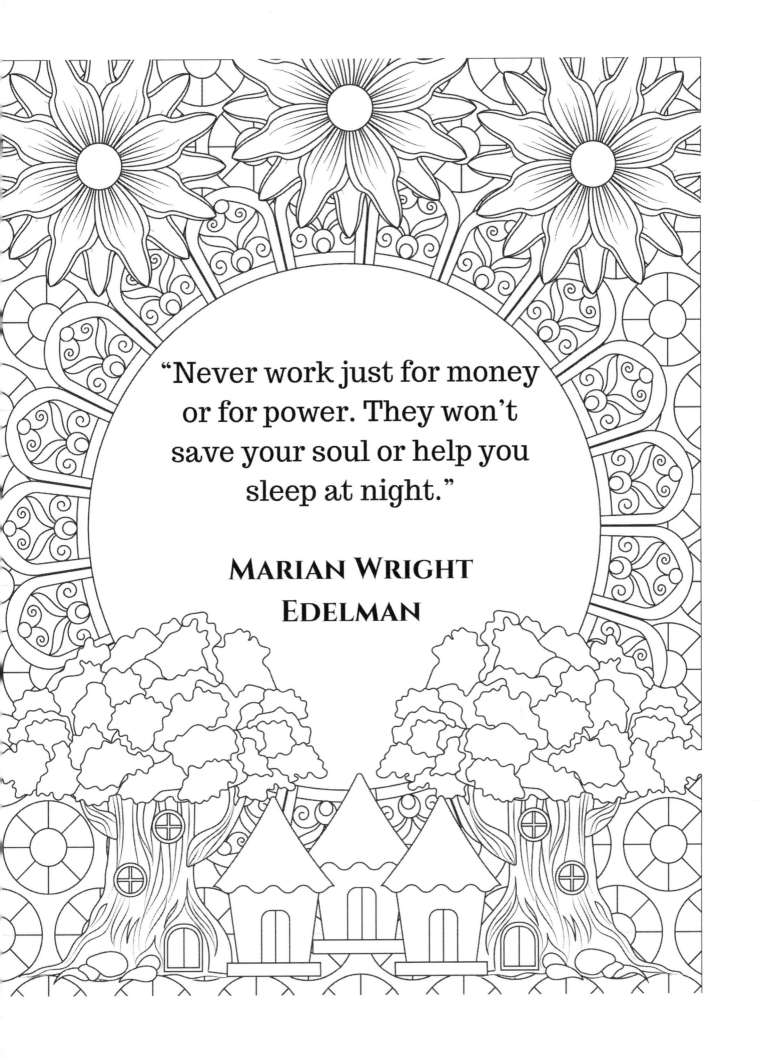

"Never work just for money or for power. They won't save your soul or help you sleep at night."

MARIAN WRIGHT EDELMAN

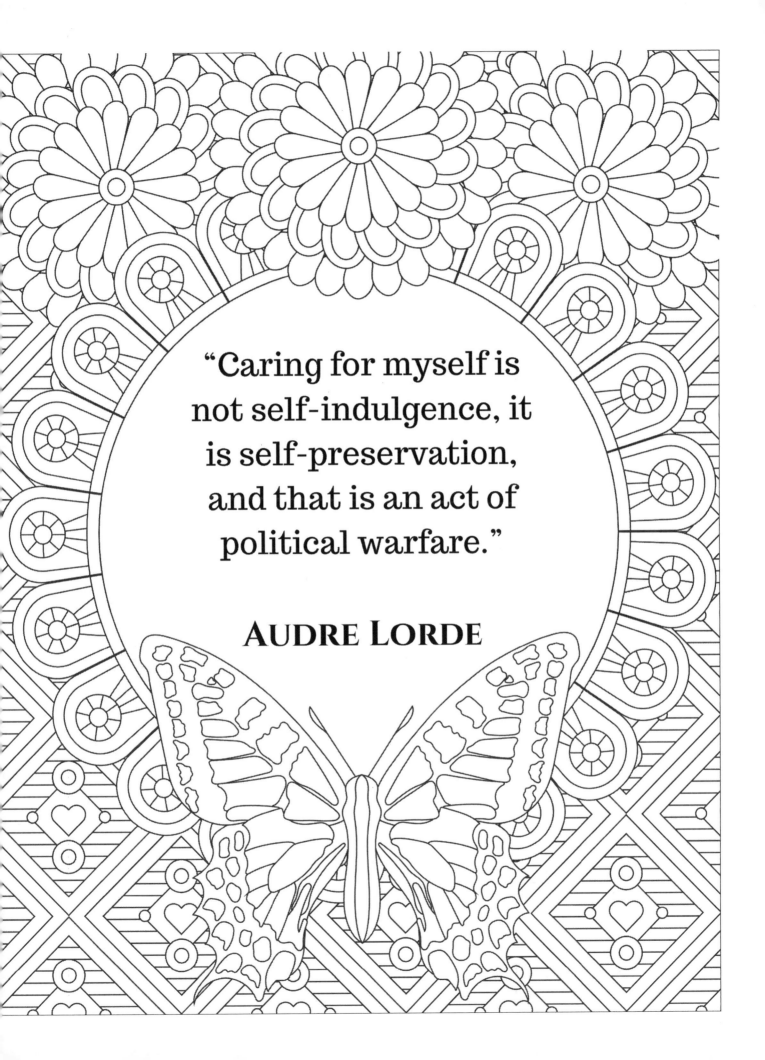

"Caring for myself is not self-indulgence, it is self-preservation, and that is an act of political warfare."

AUDRE LORDE

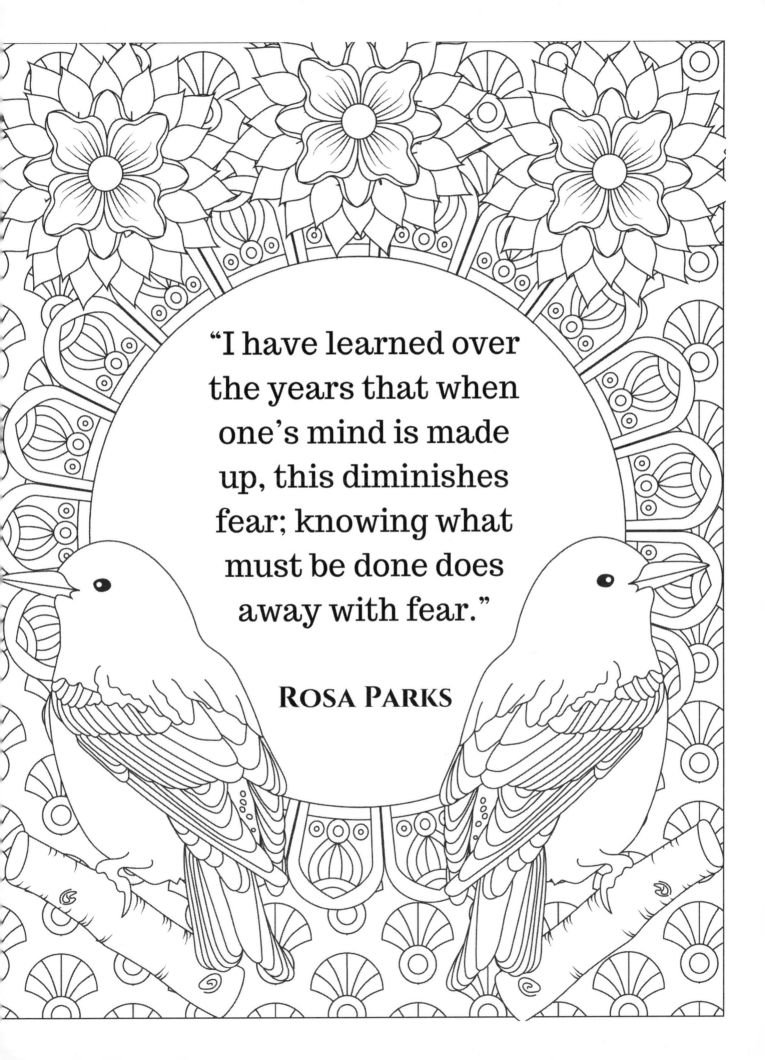

"I have learned over the years that when one's mind is made up, this diminishes fear; knowing what must be done does away with fear."

ROSA PARKS

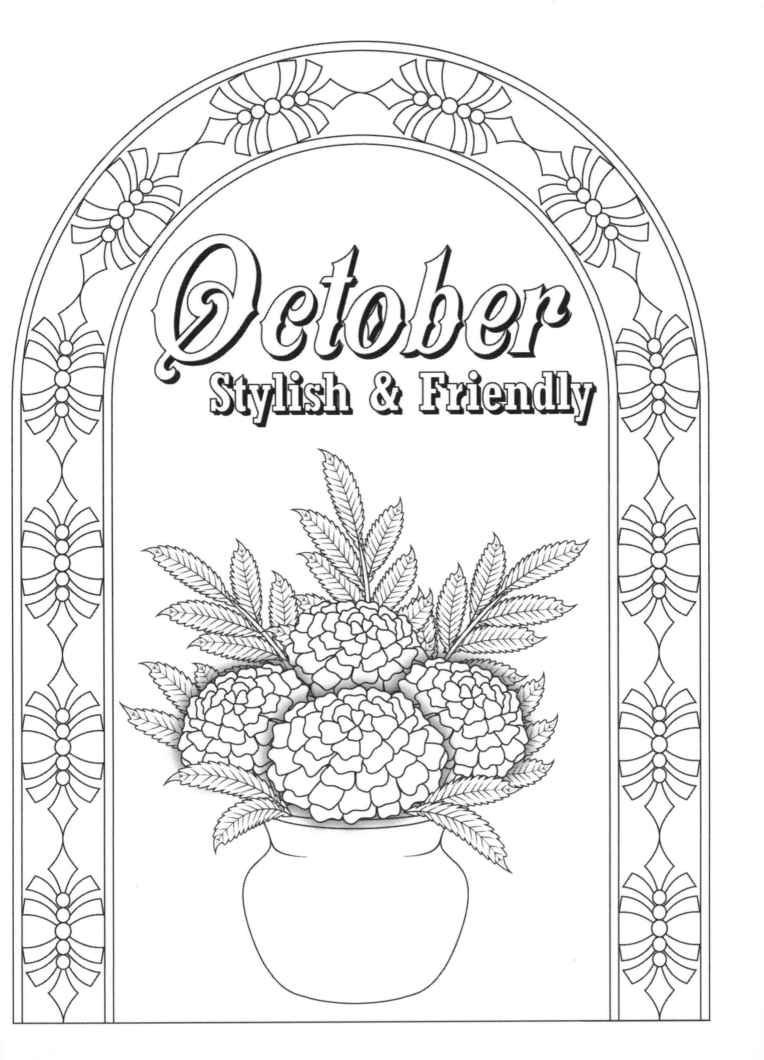

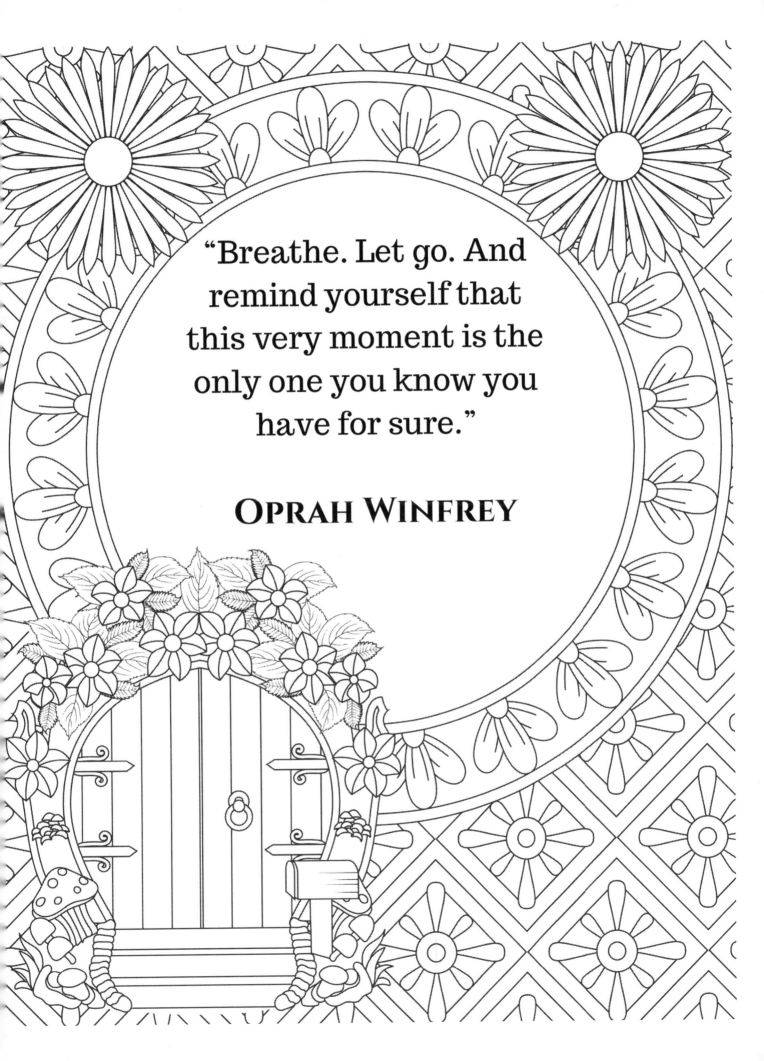

"Breathe. Let go. And remind yourself that this very moment is the only one you know you have for sure."

OPRAH WINFREY

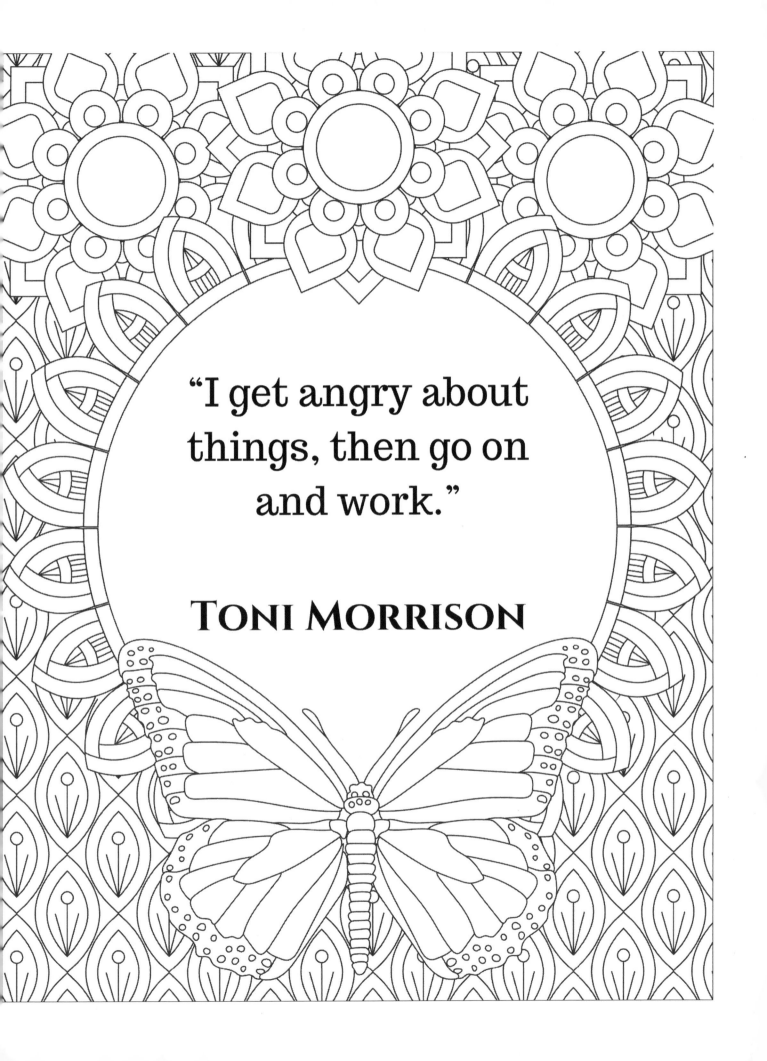

"I get angry about things, then go on and work."

TONI MORRISON

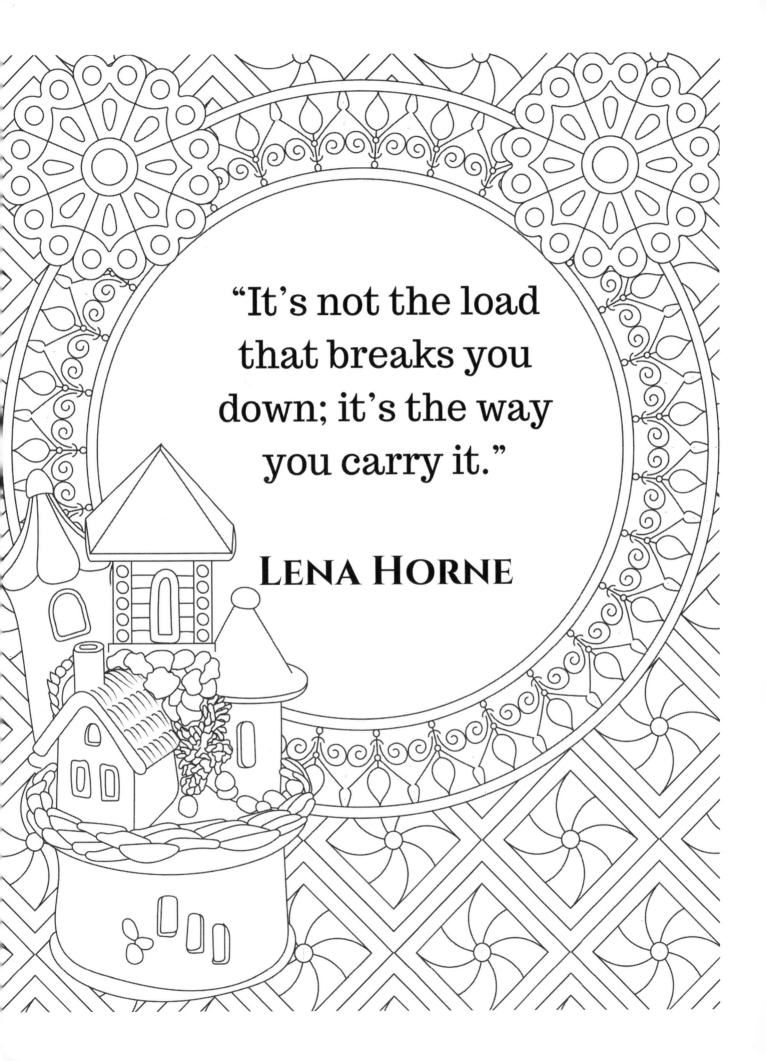

"It's not the load
that breaks you
down; it's the way
you carry it."

LENA HORNE

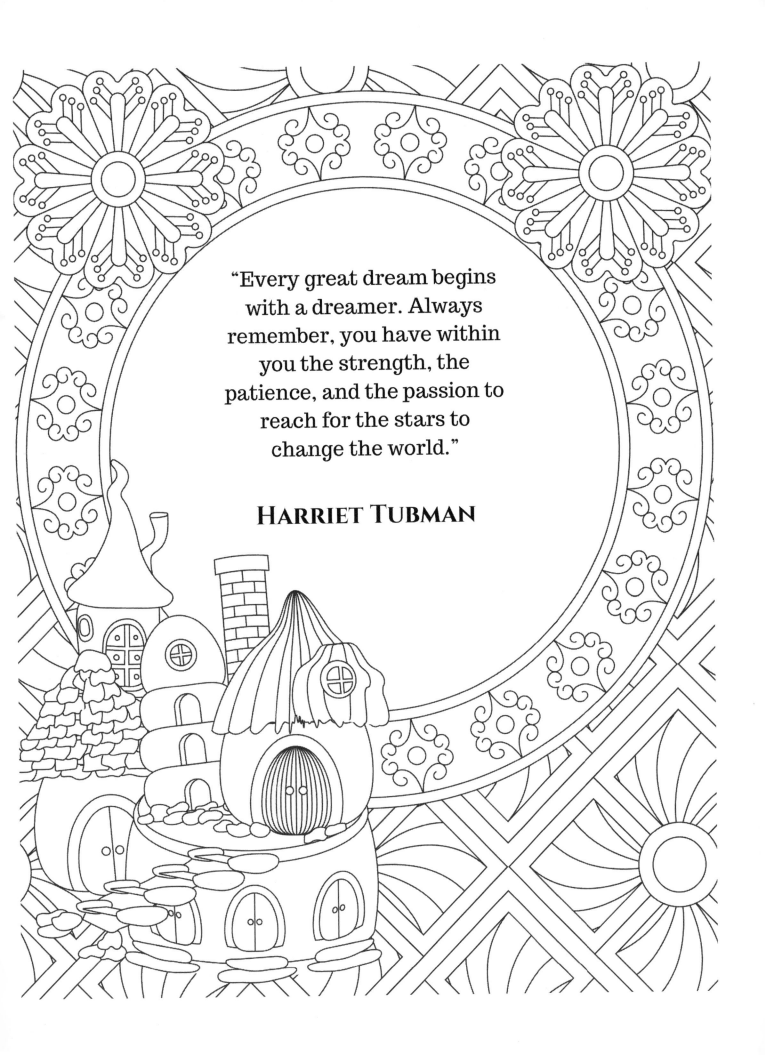

"Every great dream begins
with a dreamer. Always
remember, you have within
you the strength, the
patience, and the passion to
reach for the stars to
change the world."

HARRIET TUBMAN

N. D. Jones, Ed.D. is a USA Today bestselling author who lives in Maryland with her husband and two young adult children. In her desire to see more novels with positive, sexy, and three-dimensional black characters as soul mates, friends, and lovers, she took on that challenge herself. Along with the fantasy romance series Forever Yours, and a contemporary romance trilogy, The Styles of Love, she has authored three paranormal romance series: Winged Warriors, Death and Destiny, and Dragon Shifter Romance, and an urban fantasy duology: Feline Nation.

Connect with N.D. at www.ndjonesparanormalpleasure.com

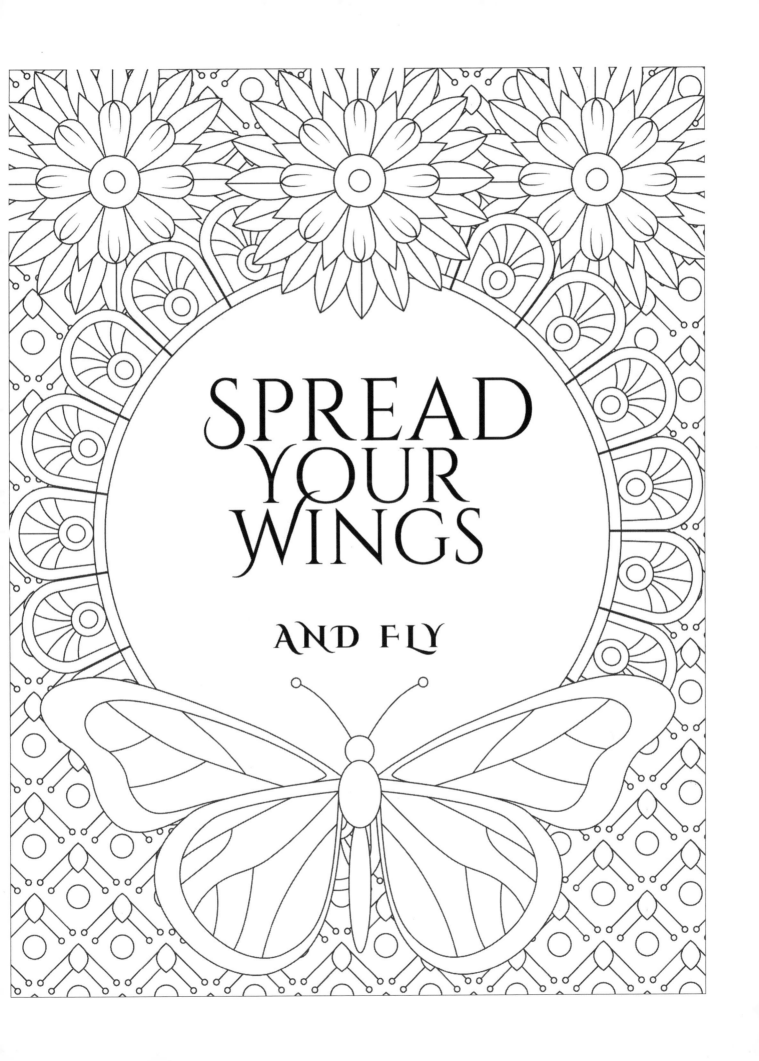

Books by N. D. Jones

Resilience (Self-Care)
The Color of My Resilience: A Guided Self-Care Journal for Black Men (Book 1)
The Color of My Resilience: A Guided Self-Care Journal for Black Women (Book 2)

Fantasy in Black (Coloring Book)
Spread Your Wings and Fly: Black Women Fairies Coloring Book
Be UnBound: Black Men Angels Coloring Book
The Beauty of Black Mermaids Coloring Book

Winged Warriors Trilogy (Paranormal Romance)
Fire, Fury, Faith (Book 1)
Heat, Hunt, Hope (Book 2)
Lies, Lust, Love (Book 3)

Death and Destiny Trilogy (Paranormal Romance)
Of Fear and Faith (Book 1)
Of Beasts and Bonds (Book 2)
Of Deception and Divinity (Book 3)
Death and Destiny: The Complete Series

Forever Yours Series (Fantasy Romance)
Bound Souls (Book 1)
Fated Path (Book 2)

Dragon Shifter Romance (Standalone Novels)
Stones of Dracontias: The Bloodstone Dragon
Dragon Lore and Love: Isis and Osiris

The Styles of Love Trilogy (Contemporary Romance)
The Perks of Higher Ed (Book 1)
The Wish of Xmas Present (Book 2)
The Gift of Second Chances (Book 3)
Rhythm and Blue Skies: Malcolm and Sky's Complete Story
The Styles of Love Trilogy: The Complete Series

Sins of the Sister **(Dark Fantasy Short Story)**

Fairy Tale Fatale Series (Urban Fantasy)
Crimson Hunter: A Red Riding Hood Reimagining

Books by N. D. Jones

Feline Nation Duology (Urban Fantasy)
A Queen's Pride (Book 1)
Mafdet's Claws (Book 2)

References

Breaking isolation: Self care and community care tools for our people. (2017, January 27). Retrieved February 26, 2021, from https://alp.org/breaking-isolation-self-care-and-community-care-tools-our-people

Brown, C. (2019, March 21). 25 Inspiring Quotes By Strong Black Women. Retrieved January 17, 2021, from https://medium.com/@ghostwriter.cheryl/25-inspiring-quotes-by-strong-black-women-8fd48819f244

Made in the USA
Middletown, DE
14 October 2022

12730383R00051